Maths
Key Stage 1 Practice Papers

Steve Mills and Hilary Koll

Write your name in the box before you start using this book.

Name

Summary of practice paper scores

When you have done each practice test an adult will mark it for you.
Then you or the adult can write your scores in these boxes.

Maths Test Level 2 score

Maths Test Level 3 score

Note for teachers and parents

The Schofield & Sims Practice Papers have been written by teachers, for use at school and at home. Both design and content are similar to the National Curriculum Key Stage tests (SATs) used in schools. You can ensure that the practice papers are used properly by reading with the child the sections **Welcome to this book** (page 2) and **What to do** (page 5). Full instructions designed for you, the adult helper, are provided in the pull-out section at the centre of this book: remove this and read it before the child tries Maths Test Level 2. Help the child during the test by reading out the directions and the oral questions provided (see pull-out section), and by marking the completed papers (answers and mark schemes are on pages 36 to 41). You can get an idea of the educational level at which the child is working using the charts on page 42. The separate Revision Guide (page numbers appear alongside each answer) enables children to revise independently for the tests: see back cover for full details.

Schofield & Sims

Contents

Pages for the child

The first paper in this book is Maths Test Level 2.
This will be the first test you try.
The second paper is Maths Test Level 3. It is more difficult.
You can read more about the tests on page 5.

Pages for teachers and parents

This section needs to be pulled out from the middle of the book by an adult before you start the first test. It begins after page 22.

These pages are for an adult to read.
They have been written for the adult who is going to help you.

In the middle of this book there are some pages that tell the adult what to do.
These pages are called **Instructions for teachers and parents**.
Answers to the tests are also given.
An adult can use the answers to mark the tests after you have done them.

What to do

The questions

- The first few questions will be read out loud.
  The adult who is helping you will read them to you.
- The adult will find the questions in the middle of this book.
  Before you start, ask the adult to pull these pages out.
- You read the other questions yourself.
  The adult will help you with difficult words.
- Read carefully what each question asks you to do.

Your answers

- Try hard to answer all the questions.
- Write your answers in the spaces.
- If you cannot do a question, try the next one.
- At the end, go back and check your work.
- If you need to do any working out, you can use any space on a page.

Timing

- The tests are **not** timed. Each one will take about 45 minutes.

After you finish a practice paper

- Ask an adult to mark your paper. The answers are on pages 36 to 41.
- Write your score in the box on page 3.
- If you did well on Maths Test Level 2, you could try Maths Test Level 3.
- Talk about this with the adult who is helping you.
- Did you get some questions wrong? Don't worry.
  The separate Revision Guide will help!
  Beside each answer there is a Revision Guide page number.
  After the test, the adult will help you to look it up.
  Then you can revise the topic.

Remember

- **Don't read the questions before the test.**
- **Don't look at the answers.**
- **Listen carefully to what the adult says or reads aloud.**
- **Think about each question.**
- **Try your best to answer it.**

**Do not turn over this page until you are ready to
start Maths Test Level 2.**

Maths Test Level 2

The first five questions will be read to you by an adult.

The adult will read them from the pull-out pages.

1

a

2

b

3

litres

metres

kilograms

minutes

c

I can measure the length of a room in _____ .

4

d

5

days

e

Do not turn over the page until the adult tells you to.

The rest of the questions are written down.

Read them carefully.

6   Look at these cards.

| 2 | 1 |

| 4 | 6 | 5 |

Pick two cards to make a number **more than 60**.

| 6 | 5 |

Pick two cards to make a number **less than 15**.

| | |

7 Write a number in the box to make this correct.

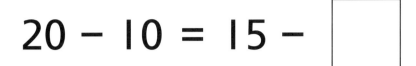

$$20 - 10 = 15 - \boxed{}$$

8 These numbers are not in order.

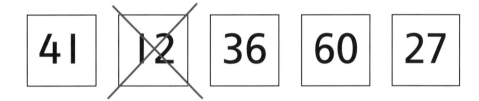

Write the numbers in order.

One has been done for you.

12				
smallest				**largest**

9 This bar chart shows what some children like doing best on Saturdays.

How many children liked **watching tv** best?

3 children liked shopping best.

Show this on the bar chart.

10

odd numbers	even numbers
17	15
31	42
25	12
23	30

Draw a ring around the number that is in the wrong place.

11   Fill in the missing numbers.

6	16		36	

12   Jack eats half of these biscuits.

How many does he eat?

Jack eats [   ] biscuits .

13 | Here are some cards.

Use **one** card to make this number sentence correct.

12 ☐ 3 = 9

Use **one** card to make this number sentence correct.

15 = 5 ☐ 10

14   There are **10** sweets in each bag.

How many sweets are there altogether?

15 | This shows the prices of some ice creams.

Hulk 35p

Star 45p

Brill 55p

Creamy 40p

Which **2** ice creams together cost **exactly £1**?

| and |

How many Creamy ice creams
can you buy for **exactly £2**?

16   Here is a plan of a town.

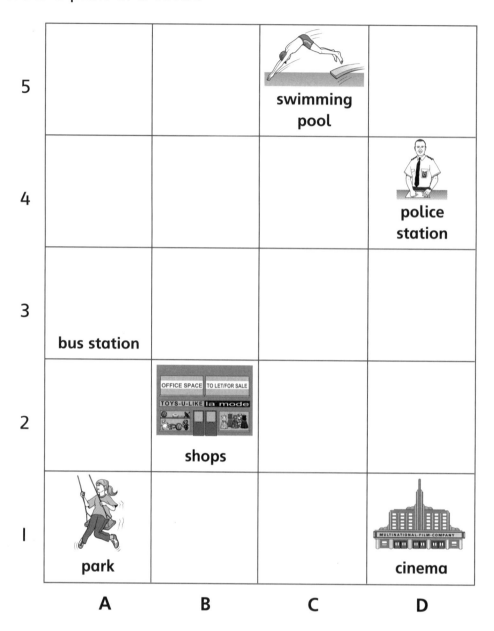

Use the plan to help you complete this table.

cinema	D1
bus station	A3
swimming pool	
	B2

17 | Look at this number pattern.

2   4   6   8   10   12   14   16   18

Make a different pattern with the number **12** in it.
Write your number pattern on the line.

_____

18 | Write a number in the box to make this correct.

100   =   46   +   ☐

19   Lisa has these coins in her pocket.

How much money has she?   [   ] p

She gives 25p to her sister.

How much has she now?   [   ] p

20   Here are some number cards.

38

35

59

47

56

54

Which of these numbers is **nearest to 50**?

Which of these numbers is an **odd number smaller than 40**?

21   How much juice is in the jug?

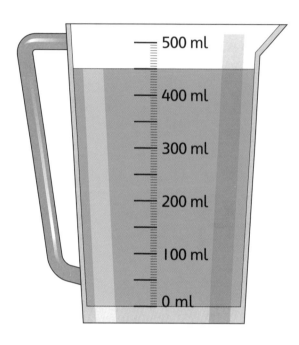

ml

22   Here is part of a number pattern.

Where would **38** go?

Write **38** in the correct place.

23 Look at this pictogram.

Colours of sweets in a bag of Whizzos

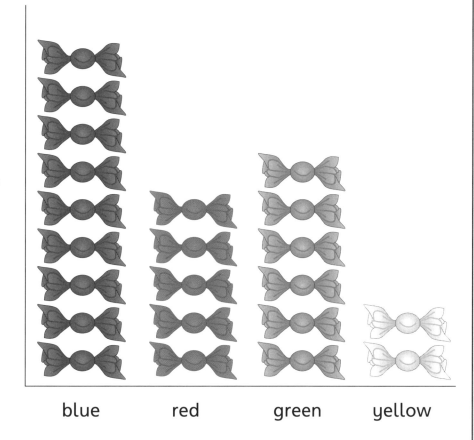

number of
sweets

blue   red   green   yellow

colours

How many **green** sweets were in the bag?

How many sweets were in the bag altogether?

This is the end of Maths Test Level 2.
Ask an adult to mark your answers.

You might be asked to try Maths Test Level 3 another time.

Maths Test Level 3

The first five questions will be read to you by an adult.

The adult will read them from the pull-out pages.

1

a

2

metres

b

3

c

Schofield&Sims

Maths

Key Stage 1 Practice Papers

Instructions for teachers and parents

Pull this centre section from the practice papers book, and read it before you talk to the child about doing the maths practice papers. You should also read with the child the pages **Welcome to this book** (practice papers page 2) and **What to do** (page 5).

Introduction

Maths Tests Levels 2 and 3 are similar to the tests that children take at school at the end of Year 2. Maths Test Level 2 is the easier of the two papers, and the child should try this first. After you have marked the level 2 test you can decide, using the guidance provided, whether or not the child should have a go at Maths Test Level 3. If the child is likely to find it too difficult, and therefore discouraging, it might be best not to try. Further guidance is provided below and on page 42.

Maths Test Level 2 begins with you reading out five questions to the child. These five questions are referred to as the 'oral questions'. The child writes his or her answers on pages 6 and 7 of the practice papers book.

Maths Test Level 2 oral questions

Before you start
As you begin, tell the child:
- **I am going to read out five questions for you to answer.**
- **I will read each question twice.**
- **If you want to hear the question a third time, ask me to read it again.**
- **Listen very carefully to each question.**
- **You have plenty of time to write your answer.**
- **You should write your answer in the book. I will tell you where on the page to write it.**
- **If you make a mistake, cross it out or rub it out. Then write your answer clearly.**

During the test
Ask the child to open the book at page 6. Explain the following:
- **You write your answers in the boxes.**
- **The letter below the box tells you which box to use for which question.**
- **You can use any of the white space outside the boxes for your working out.**

Tell the child: **Now we are going to start the test.**
Read each of the questions below *twice*, leaving a short gap in between.
Wait until the child has answered the question before you go on to the next one.

1.	**Find box a.**
	Add these three numbers: four and four and four.
	Write your answer in box a.

please turn over

2.	Find box b.
	Write down an even number between forty-one and fifty-one.
	Write your answer in box b.
3.	Look at the words in box c.
	The words say: litres metres kilograms minutes
	One of the words completes this sentence:
	'I can measure the length of a room in . . .'
	Tick the correct word.
4.	Look at the next page.
	Find box d.
	What number must Jack add to fifteen to get an answer of twenty-four?
	Write your answer in box d.
5.	Find box e.
	How many days are there in one week?
	Write your answer in box e.

As soon as the child has finished, introduce the written questions as described below.

Maths Test Level 2 written questions

Before you start
Explain to the child the following points:
- The rest of the questions are written down in the book.
- You have to read each question and work out the answer.
- You write your answer in the space in the book.
- Don't guess the answer. Read what you have to do.
- You can use any spaces on the page for your working out.
- Show your working out if you are asked to. You might get an extra mark for it.
- If you make a mistake you can change your answer by rubbing or crossing it out.
- If you cannot do a question, leave it. Go back to it later if you can. Go on to the next question.
- Answer as many questions as possible.
- Take as much time as you need.
- When you have finished, check your answers.

Tell the child: **Now turn over to page 8 and start the written questions.**

During the test
If the child is unable to read any unfamiliar words, you can provide help. However, you should not help the child with any numbers or symbols and you should not explain the questions.

The test is not timed. You should check that the child stops when he or she has done as much of the test as possible.

After the test

When the child has finished Maths Test Level 2, you can mark the test using the answers on pages 36 to 38. Then write the child's total score in the box on page 3. If the child had difficulty with any of the questions, encourage him or her to read the relevant topic in the separate Revision Guide (for details see back cover). A Revision Guide page number is given beside each answer.

If you wish, you can convert the child's score to a 'level', as described on page 42. If a child achieves level 2A on the level 2 test at school, he or she is normally entered for the level 3 test. You might like to follow this same guidance for the child you are helping. If the child achieves a score of between 19 and 30 marks on Maths Test Level 2, suggest that he or she tries Maths Test Level 3. If his or her score is lower than this, the level 3 test might be too difficult.

Maths Test Level 3 oral questions

Maths Test Level 3, like the level 2 test, begins with you reading out five questions to the child. The child writes his or her answers on pages 22 and 23 of the practice papers book.

Before you start

When you are ready to begin, tell the child:
- **I am going to read out five questions for you to answer.**
- **I will read each question twice.**
- **If you want to hear the question a third time, ask me to read it again.**
- **Listen very carefully to each question.**
- **You have plenty of time to write your answer.**
- **You should write your answer in the book. I will tell you where on the page to write it.**
- **If you make a mistake, cross it out or rub it out. Then write your answer clearly.**

During the test

Ask the child to open the book at page 22. Explain the following:
- **You write your answers in the boxes.**
- **The letter below the box tells you which box to use for which question.**
- **You can use any of the white space outside the boxes for your working out.**

Tell the child: **Now we are going to start the test.**
Read each of the questions below *twice*, leaving a short gap in between.
Wait until the child has answered the question before you go on to the next one.

1.	Find box a.
	Write the number one thousand and nine.
	Write your answer in box a.
2.	Find box b.
	How many metres are there in a kilometre?
	Write your answer in box b.

please turn over

3.	Find box c.
	In the shop there are six shelves with forty tins on each shelf.
	How many tins are there altogether?
	Write your answer in box c.
4.	Look at the next page.
	Find box d.
	Thirty children get into teams of five. How many teams are there altogether?
	Write your answer in box d.
5.	Find box e.
	I'm thinking of a number. Four is a quarter of my number. What is my number?
	Write your answer in box e.

As soon as the child has finished, introduce the written questions as described below.

Maths Test Level 3 written questions

Before you start

Explain to the child the following points:

- **The rest of the questions are written down in the book.**
- **You have to read each question and work out the answer.**
- **You write your answer in the space in the book.**
- **Don't guess the answer. Read what you have to do.**
- **You can use any spaces on the page for your working out.**
- **Show your working out if you are asked to. You might get an extra mark for it.**
- **If you make a mistake you can change your answer by rubbing or crossing it out.**
- **If you cannot do a question, leave it. Go back to it later if you can. Go on to the next question.**
- **Answer as many questions as possible.**
- **Take as much time as you need.**
- **When you have finished, check your answers.**

Tell the child: **Now turn over to page 24 and start the written questions.**

During the test

If the child is unable to read any unfamiliar words, you can provide help. However, you should not help the child with any numbers or symbols and you should not explain the questions.

The test is not timed. You should check that the child stops when he or she has done as much of the test as possible.

After the test

When the child has finished Maths Test Level 3, you can mark the test using the answers on pages 39 to 41. Write the child's total score in the box on page 3. As before, if the child had difficulty with any of the questions, encourage him or her to read the relevant topic in the Revision Guide: a page number is given beside each answer.

If you wish, you can convert the child's score to a level, as described on page 42.

This is a pull-out section from the Schofield and Sims Maths Key Stage 1 Practice Papers.
Published by Schofield and Sims Ltd, Dogley Mill, Fenay Bridge, Huddersfield HD8 0NQ, UK.
Tel 01484 607080   www.schofieldandsims.co.uk
First published in 2004   Copyright © Schofield and Sims Ltd 2004   All rights reserved.
Authors: Steve Mills and Hilary Koll   ISBN 978 07217 0952 9

4

d

5

e

Do not turn over the page until the adult tells you to.

The rest of the questions are written down.

Read them carefully.

6   One of these sticks is exactly 8cm long.

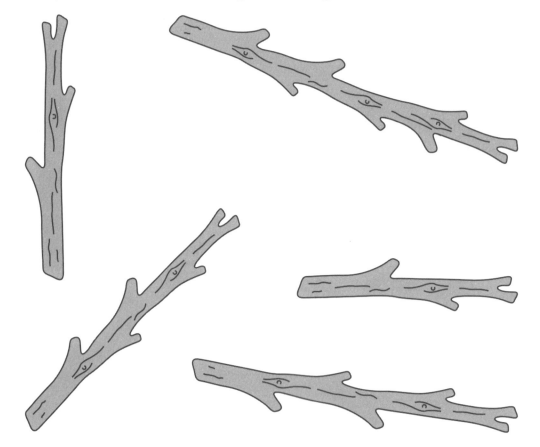

Draw a ring around the stick that is exactly 8cm long.

7   How much do these apples weigh?

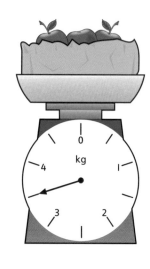

kg

8

Towers theme park

children   £4

adults   £7

How much does it cost for 3 adults and 2 children?

Show how you worked it out in the box.

The cost for 3 adults and 2 children is   £ _____ .

2 marks

9 Here are two hexagons.

Join some dots to draw a **different** hexagon.

Use a ruler.

10 Complete this number pattern.

64	half	32	half		half		half	

11   One of the squares in this pattern has been shaded.

Shade more of the squares so that **one quarter** of
the pattern has been shaded.

12   Find the difference between **34** and **19**.

Show your working here.

The difference between **34** and **19** is   .

13   Draw a ring around the **smallest** number.

156

165

148

172

127

184

14   Write numbers in the circles to make this correct.

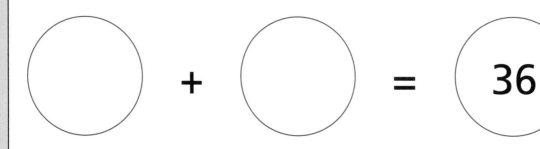

$$\bigcirc + \bigcirc = 36$$

15

The coach sets off to London at this time.

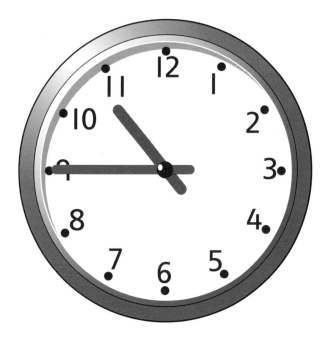

It gets to London exactly 5 hours and 15 minutes later.

Show the time on the clock when the coach gets to London.

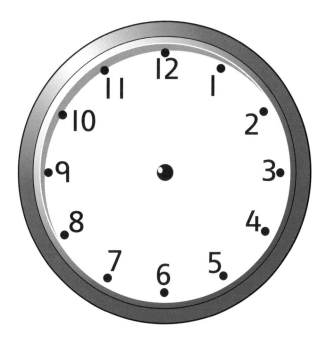

16   Add these numbers.

$$57 \quad + \quad 45 \quad + \quad 93$$

Show your working in the box.

$$57 \quad + \quad 45 \quad + \quad 93 \quad = \quad \boxed{}$$

2 marks

17   Write the missing numbers in this sequence.

2 marks

18   Here are some instructions for this trail. Complete them.

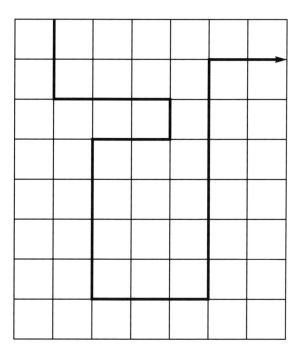

down 2

right 3

down 1

19

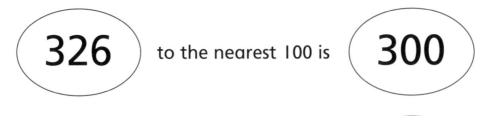

326   to the nearest 100 is   300

473   to the nearest 100 is

20   Two of the shapes are pentagons **and** have three right angles.

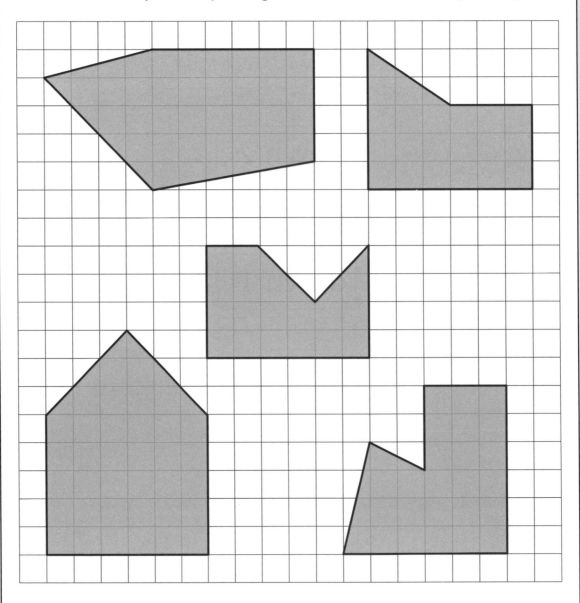

Tick (✔) each of the two shapes.

21 What number do you think the arrow is pointing to?

Write the number in the empty box.

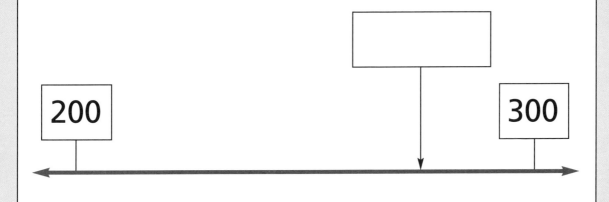

22 Draw the reflection of this shape. Use a ruler.

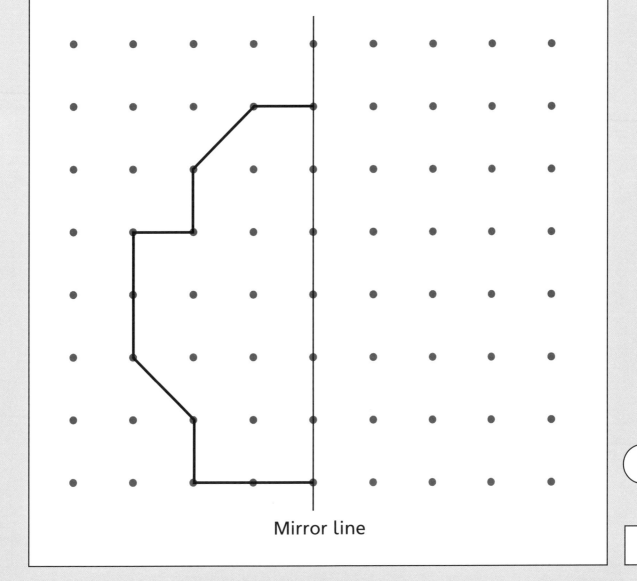

Mirror line

23 Match each question to its answer by drawing a line.

You can use an answer more than once.

6 × 5   40

20 ÷ 2   7

2 × 7   30

35 ÷ 5   10

10 × 3   14

2 marks

24 Look at this chart.

Number of ice creams sold in one week

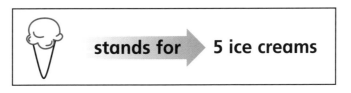

stands for ➡ 5 ice creams

Monday

Tuesday

Wednesday

Thursday

Friday

Saturday

Sunday

How many **more** ice creams were sold on **Thursday** than on **Monday**?

	ice creams

5 ice creams were sold on Sunday. Show this on the chart.

**This is the end of Maths Test Level 3.
Ask an adult to mark your answers.**

Level 2 Test answers and mark scheme

Question no.	Correct answer	Additional comments	Marks	Revision Guide links
1.	12	If the child has written a digit in reverse, for example, the reflection of 2, he or she should be given the mark, provided that it clearly shows the characteristics of a 2 rather than a 5. If the digits are in the wrong order (for example, 21 rather than 12), do not give the mark. **This applies for all the questions in the tests**.	1 mark	**Mental addition** pages 18–21
2.	42, 44, 46, 48, or 50	The child should be familiar with the term 'even number' and should know that the unit digit of an even number will be 0, 2, 4, 6 or 8.	1 mark	**Odd and even numbers** page 5
3.	metres	If the child has circled, underlined or clearly indicated metres rather than ticking it, give the mark. If more than one word has been ticked, do not give the mark.	1 mark	**Length** page 36
4.	9	A child hearing two numbers (in this case, 15 and 24) and an instruction will often add the numbers – adding here would give an answer of 39. The child must be encouraged to listen to the question carefully. It can be answered using either counting on from 15 to 24 (addition) or counting back from 24 to 15 (subtraction).	1 mark	**Mental addition** pages 18–21 **Mental subtraction** pages 22–24
5.	7		1 mark	**Time** pages 39–40
6.	12 or 14	The child should notice that the only two-digit numbers less than 15 are 12 and 14. You can use similar number cards to make up similar questions for the child to practise.	1 mark	**Numbers and their digits** page 4
7.	5	A child sometimes sees the equals sign as an instruction to do something rather than as a sign of equality (i.e. that things on either side of it should be equal). As a result, the child may be confused that there is not simply an answer to the right of it. Show the child that 20 – 10 equals 10 and 15 – 5 also equals 10.	1 mark	**Addition and subtraction facts** page 25
8.	27, 36, 41, 60	If the child has answered this question incorrectly, he or she may not fully understand the value of digits in a number (tens and units), e.g. that the 6 in 36 is worth less than the 6 in 60. Do not give a mark if the digits of any number are transposed or if any of the numbers are out of order.	1 mark	**Ordering** page 12

If the test results show that the child needs help, refer to these pages in the separate Revision Guide (see back cover for full details).

Question no.	Correct answer	Additional comments	Marks	Revision Guide links
9.	a) 5		1 mark	**Block graphs** page 55
	b) bottom 3 rectangles shaded in the shopping column	Give no mark if fewer or more rectangles are shaded.	1 mark	
10.	15	Here the child must look to see which number is incorrectly placed in the Carroll diagram. A knowledge of odd and even numbers is necessary. Give the mark if the number 15 has been indicated in some other way, e.g. written at the side or ticked.	1 mark	**Carroll diagrams** page 52 **Odd and even numbers** page 5
11.	26, 46	The child should notice that there is a pattern in the numbers given: they increase by 10. When counting on in tens, the units digit always stays the same, e.g. 7, 17, 27, 37 …	1 mark	**Counting in tens** page 8 **Number patterns** page 10
12.	7	If the child has written a digit in reverse, for example, the reflection of 7, he or she should be given the mark provided that it clearly shows the characteristics of a 7 rather than a 2.	1 mark	**Fractions** pages 15–17
13.	a) –	A child sometimes see the equals sign as an instruction to do something, rather than as a sign of equality (i.e. that things on either side of it should be equal). Here, the child might have found it confusing that 'the answer comes first'.	1 mark	**Mental subtraction** pages 22–24
	b) +		1 mark	**Mental addition** pages 18–21
14.	60	The child should be using mental methods or using facts that he or she has learned by heart to answer this question. It can be tackled by multiplication (6 lots of 10 or 6 × 10) or addition (counting on in tens).	1 mark	**Mental addition** pages 18–21 **Multiplication** page 26 **Counting in tens** page 8
15.	a) Star and Brill	The child may use trial and error for this question. To cut down the number of options, he or she may notice that the Creamy ice cream costs 40p and, when added to any other ice cream, will give an amount ending in 5p.	1 mark	**Mental addition** pages 18–21 **Addition and subtraction facts** page 25
	b) 5	Encourage the child to explain to you how he or she worked out the answer to this question, e.g. *I added 40 five times*, or *I know that 4 x 5 = 20 so 40 x 5 = 200*.	1 mark	**Multiplication** page 26
16.	a) C5		1 mark	**Positions** page 49
	b) shops	Help the child with writing the word 'shops' if necessary.	1 mark	

Question no.	Correct answer	Additional comments	Marks	Revision Guide links
17.	Any number sequence containing the number 12, e.g. 9, 10, 11, 12, 13 ... or 6, 12, 18 ... or 2, 12, 22, 32 ...	Such sequences can be practised by counting forwards or backwards from a start number in equal steps and predicting whether particular numbers will be in the sequence. Do not give a mark for the same sequence or part of it, e.g. do not give a mark for 6, 8, 10, 12, 14 ...	1 mark	Counting on in ones, twos, tens, fives pages 6, 7, 8, 9 Number patterns page 10
18.	54	If the answer given was 64, encourage the child to notice that 46 + 64 = 110.	1 mark	Mental addition pages 18–21 Mental subtraction pages 22–24
19.	a) 88p	The total of all the coins is 88p. If the child experiences difficulty in recognising pictures of coins, he or she could place real coins onto the pictures and then count the coins.	1 mark	Money pages 34–35 Mental addition pages 18–21
	b) 63p	Any method is acceptable for giving a mark, provided that the answer is correct, e.g. counting back 25 from 88, subtracting 20 and then 5, counting up from 25 to 88, using a number line, etc.	1 mark	Mental subtraction pages 22–24
20.	a) 47	If the child answered 54, draw a number line marked in ones from 45 to 55, i.e. 45 46 **47** 48 49 **50** 51 52 53 **54** 55 and point out the relative positions of 54 and 47.	1 mark	Ordering pages 12–13
	b) 35		1 mark	Odd and even numbers page 5
21.	450ml		1 mark	Capacity page 38
22.	38 goes in the first star.	The child needs to be able to count back from the numbers in the sequence. You can give him or her similar sequences for practice.	1 mark	Counting in ones page 6 Ordering pages 12–13
23.	a) 6		1 mark	Pictograms page 54
	b) 22	The child should have added all the different colours together, i.e. 9 + 5 + 6 + 2 = 22	1 mark	

- As you mark each question on the practice paper, write the mark in the circle beside it.
- Total the marks for each page, and write them in the box at the foot of the page.
- When you have marked every page, add up all the marks (maximum 30) and write the total in the pink box at the foot of page 21. Copy this total to the summary box on page 3.
- Work out the child's level (see page 42) before deciding whether to give him or her Maths Test Level 3.

Level 3 Test answers and mark scheme

Question no.	Correct answer	Additional comments	Marks	Revision Guide links
1.	1009	Children often experience difficulty in writing numbers with zeros as digits, e.g. 109, 1009, 10009, etc. This shows a lack of understanding of place value (knowing what the digits in a number represent), e.g. hundreds, tens and units.	1 mark	**Numbers and their digits** page 4 **Ordering** page 13
2.	1000	The child should know by heart that there are 1000m in 1km, 100cm in 1m, etc.	1 mark	**Length** page 36
3.	240	If the child answered 46, he or she has added the numbers rather than multiplied them. Discuss the context and sketch a drawing of the shelves if necessary.	1 mark	**Multiplication** page 26
4.	6	The child should know multiplication and division facts related to the 5 times table.	1 mark	**Tables facts** page 27 **Division facts** page 29
5.	16	The child may give the answer 1 as a result of simply hearing the number 4 together with the word 'quarter' and finding a quarter of 4. Encourage the child to listen carefully to the question. Ask 'If four is one quarter, how many is two quarters?' etc.	1 mark	**Multiplication** page 26 **Fractions** pages 15–17 **Number problems** pages 32–33
6.		Make sure that the child is using a ruler properly.	1 mark	**Length** page 36
7.	$3\frac{1}{2}$ kg		1 mark	**Mass** page 37
8.	29	Give 2 marks for the correct answer. Give one mark for correctly finding the cost for either 3 adults (£21) or 2 children (£8) and attempting to add the two numbers.	max. 2 marks	**Multiplication** page 26 **Number problems** pages 32–33
9.	Any shape with 6 straight sides.	Give no mark if the shape has fewer or more than 6 sides.	1 mark	**2-D shapes** pages 42–43
10.	16, 8, 4		1 mark	**Doubling and halving** page 30

Question no.	Correct answer	Additional comments	Marks	Revision Guide links
11.	The child should shade 2 more of the squares so that 3 are shaded in total.	Encourage the child to see that 3 out of 12 has the same value as one quarter.	1 mark	**Fractions** pages 15–17
12.	15	The child might answer this question by first subtracting 20 from 34 and then adding 1, or he or she might count up from 19 to 20, then 30 and to 34. Give the mark however the child gets the answer.	1 mark	**Mental subtraction** pages 22–24
13.	127		1 mark	**Ordering** pages 12–13
14.	Any 2 numbers that add to make 36, e.g. 1 + 35, 2 + 34, 6 + 30 ...	Always encourage the child to check his or her answers.	1 mark	**Mental addition** pages 18–21
15.	Hands on the clock showing 4 o'clock.	Do not give the mark if both hands are identical in length.	1 mark	**Time** pages 39–41
16.	195	Give one mark if the working shows a suitable method for adding two of the numbers and an attempt to add the third, or an attempt to add all three numbers at once.	max. 2 marks	**Mental addition** pages 18–21
17.	205, 195	Give one mark for each number, so if one answer is incorrect, give only one mark for this question.	max. 2 marks	**Mental subtraction** pages 22–24 **Ordering** pages 12–13
18.	left 2, down 4, right 3, up 6, right 2	Give only one mark if *one* of the instructions is incorrect.	max. 2 marks	**Positions** page 49 **Directions** page 50
19.	500	The child should realise that 473 is closer to 500 than 400. Use a number line marked in tens from 400 to 500. Ask the child where 450, then 470 then 473 would go.	1 mark	**Number lines** page 14

Question no.	Correct answer	Additional comments	Marks	Revision Guide links
20.	The top right and bottom left shapes are pentagons and have three right angles:	Encourage the child to consider each criterion in turn, e.g. first cross out any shapes that are not pentagons. Of the remainder, find two with three right angles.	1 mark	**2-D shapes** pages 42–43 **Right angles and turns** page 48
21.	Any number between 270 and 280 inclusive.	Split the line in half and then in half again to help the child estimate.	1 mark	**Number lines** page 14
22.		If the child got this question wrong, use a mirror to show him or her the correct reflection.	1 mark	**Symmetry** pages 46–47
23.	6 × 5 — 40 20 ÷ 2 — 7 2 × 7 — 30 35 ÷ 5 — 10 10 × 3 — 14	Give one mark if one match is incorrect.	max. 2 marks	**Multiplication** page 26 **Division** page 28 **Tables facts** page 27 **Division facts** page 29
24.	a) 10	The child needs to realise that one symbol on the chart stands for 5 items.	1 mark	**Pictograms** page 54
	b) 1 ice cream symbol drawn.	Again, the child needs to realise that one symbol on the chart stands for 5 items.	1 mark	

- As you mark each question on the practice paper, write the mark in the circle beside it.
- Total the marks for each page, and write them in the box at the foot of the page.
- When you have marked every page, add up all the marks (maximum 30) and write the total in the pink box at the foot of page 35. Copy this total to the summary box on page 3.

How to convert scores to levels

National Curriculum levels measure a child's progress in each subject. Each level is like one step. As children continue their education, they move up through the levels. Children within Key Stage 1 are working at a level somewhere between levels 1 and 3.

You can get an idea of the level a child is working at from the total scores that he or she obtains on the practice papers.

Score

Maths Test Level 2	[ ]

out of 30

Level and grade:	[ ]	

Maths Test Level 3	[ ]

out of 30

Level 3 achieved?	[ ]	Tick if child scores 11 or more

Maths Test Level 2

When a child has taken the level 2 test at school, the teacher marks the test. He or she then uses a chart similar to the one below to decide what level the child is working at.

Child's total score (maximum 30)	0–4	5–7	8–13	14–18	19–30
Level and grade	No level achieved	Level 1 achieved	Level 2C achieved	Level 2B achieved	Level 2A achieved

You can use the same chart to work out what the child's level might be, based on his or her score on the Maths Level 2 practice paper. For example, if a child had a score of 6 marks, he or she would have achieved level 1.

Should this child take Maths Test Level 3?

If a child achieves level 2A on the level 2 test at school, he or she is normally entered for the level 3 test. You might like to follow this same guidance for the child you are helping. If the child achieves a score of between 19 and 30 marks on the Maths Test Level 2 practice paper, suggest that he or she tries Maths Test Level 3. If his or her score is lower than this, the level 3 practice paper might be too difficult.

Maths Test Level 3

After the child has taken the Maths Test Level 3 practice paper, use the chart below to work out what the child's level might be, based on his or her score. For example, if a child had a score of 6 marks on this paper, he or she would not have achieved level 3.

Child's total score (maximum 30)	0–10	11–30
Level	Level 3 not achieved	Level 3 achieved

You can make a note of the child's scores and levels in the boxes at the top of this page.

Please note

Any levels obtained from the Schofield & Sims Key Stage 1 Maths Practice Papers are only valid if the child is nearing the end of Key Stage 1 and has done the test under proper test conditions, without reference to the separate Revision Guide or other maths materials. **The level obtained is only an *indication* of the level at which the child is working, and it may not match the level given by the child's teacher.**

Published by Schofield and Sims Ltd,
Dogley Mill, Fenay Bridge, Huddersfield HD8 0NQ, UK

Tel 01484 607080
www.schofieldandsims.co.uk   —

First published in 2004
Reprinted 2005 (twice), 2006, 2007
Copyright © Schofield and Sims Ltd 2004

Authors: Steve Mills and Hilary Koll (contact@cmeprojects.com)

Steve Mills and Hilary Koll have asserted their moral right under the Copyright,
Designs and Patents Act, 1988, to be identified as the authors of this work.

British Library Cataloguing in Publication Data
A catalogue record for this book is available from the British Library.

Edited by Carolyn Richardson Publishing Services (cr@publiserve.fsnet.co.uk)

Designed by Oxford Designers & Illustrators

Printed in the UK by Wyndeham Gait Ltd, Grimsby

ISBN 978 07217 0952 9

The Schofield & Sims Revision Guides help children to revise for the Key Stage tests (SATs) by guiding them through what they have already learned at school on a topic-by-topic basis. The Guides have been written by teachers and are designed for children to use independently at home or in school. They are comprehensive and provide excellent value for money.

The **Key Stage 1 Maths Practice Papers** contained in this book are similar in both appearance and content to the actual Key Stage 1 mathematics tests and give children a valuable opportunity to prepare for them. The papers included are:

- Maths Level 2   ● Maths Level 3

Full instructions are contained in a pull-out section, designed for parents and teachers. Detailed mark schemes are also provided, together with tables that give an indication of the level at which the child is working. The answers are cross-referenced to the Revision Guide, which children can refer to for help.

The separate Key Stage 1 Maths Revision Guide provides a clear explanation of every topic likely to be covered in the Key Stage 1 mathematics tests. All the topics are linked to the National Numeracy Strategy, and these curricular links are displayed in an easy-to-read Curriculum chart. The coverage of each topic includes worked examples of questions and processes, a useful summary of key points to remember, and 'Test yourself!' questions and answers to check children's understanding. Colourful illustrations and diagrams help to make revision simple and a glossary defines the key words related to the subject. Helpful 'tips for tests' ensure that children perform to the best of their ability in the tests.

Revision Guide
ISBN 978 07217 0951 2

Also available:

At Key Stage 2

Revision Guide	Practice Papers	Revision Guide	Practice Papers	Revision Guide	Practice Papers
ISBN 978 07217 0953 6	ISBN 978 07217 0954 3	ISBN 978 07217 0957 4	ISBN 978 07217 0958 1	ISBN 978 07217 0955 0	ISBN 978 07217 0956 7

For further information, see **www.schofieldandsims.co.uk** or **telephone 01484 607080**

ISBN 978-07217-0952-9

9 780721 709529

Price: £1.95
Key Stage 1
Age range: 5–7 years